MOOMINTROLL'S
book of thoughts

ILLUSTRATIONS AND QUOTATIONS BY TOVE JANSSON
TEXT BY SAMI MALILA
TRANSLATION BY PAMELA KASKINEN

SELF
MADE
HERO

Excerpts and illustrations by Tove Jansson © Moomin Characters Ltd., Finland
Text © Sami Malila and WSOY
Original title: "Muumipeikon mietekirja"
First published in Finnish by Werner Söderström Corporation (WSOY)
 in 2007, Helsinki, Finland
Translation into English © Pamela Kaskinen

First published in English by SelfMadeHero in 2010
A division of Metro Media Ltd
5 Upper Wimpole Street London W1G 6BP
www.selfmadehero.com

Publishing Director: Emma Hayley
Marketing Director: Doug Wallace
Layout designer: Kurt Young
With thanks to: Nick de Somogyi and Jane Laporte

This work has been published with the financial assistance of
FILI – Finnish Literature Exchange

FINNISH LITERATURE EXCHANGE

A CIP record for this book is available from the British Library

978-1-906838-22-5

10 9 8 7 6 5 4 3 2 1

Printed and bound in England

To the Reader

THE BELOVED MOOMIN STORIES OF
TOVE JANSSON ARE FULL OF THRILLING
ADVENTURES, EXUBERANT HUMOUR, ETERNAL TRUTHS
AND TIMELESS WISDOM.

THIS BOOK OF THOUGHTS IS A COLLECTION OF THE
UPLIFTING MUSINGS OF THE TENDER AND SENTIMENTAL
YOUNG MOOMINTROLL.

MOOMINTROLL IS INNOCENT AND SINCERE, WITH A
SHARP EYE FOR THE SMALL BEAUTIFUL THINGS IN LIFE.
HE IS ALWAYS CONSIDERATE OF OTHERS, EVEN THOSE OF
US WHO ARE MOST QUIET AND UNASSUMING.

WE HOPE YOU ENJOY THE
ENCHANTING INSIGHTS OF MOOMINTROLL'S
BOOK OF THOUGHTS!

Excerpts and illustrations are from the following WSOY editions of the Moomin books, translated from the original Swedish into Finnish:

MUUMIPEIKKO JA PYRSTÖTÄHTI

TAIKURIN HATTU

VAARALLINEN JUHANNUS

TAIKATALVI

NÄKYMÄTÖN LAPSI JA MUITA KERTOMUKSIA

MUUMIPAPAN UROTYÖT

MUUMIPAPPA JA MERI

MUUMILAAKSON MARRASKUU

Contents

Friendship and Understanding

SNUFKIN was his best friend. Of course, he was also incredibly fond of the Snork Maiden, but it wasn't the same thing at all – seeing as how she was a girl.

MOOMINTROLL closed his eyes and surmised, "How different we all are, really."

"MAMMA," whispered Moomintroll. "What has happened to her? Why has she become so mean?"

"Who?" replied Moominmamma.

"The Groke. Has someone done something to her to make her become as she is?"

As soon as Moomintroll's snout reached the surface of the water, he turned and swam towards Snufkin's boat.

"Hello!" he said, grabbing on to the side of the boat. "I sure am glad to see you!"

"BY the end of the hairs on my long, long tail!"
Moomintroll whispered in fervent astonishment.

THEN the creature with the ridiculous eyebrows became
quite agitated, picked himself up and vanished.

"Good gracious, now what do I do?" said Moomintroll.
"He'll live for an entire year underneath the sink without
ever knowing that I was only trying to be friendly!"

MOOMINTROLL made a friendly, yet preoccupied sound.

NOW everything was spoiled. One ought to have the right to discover a secret, keep it under wraps for a while, and then spring it on everyone. But if you live in a family, there is no point trying to have secrets or arrange surprises of any kind. Everyone knows everything, right from the start, and that's no fun at all.

"I think I'm beginning to understand now," said Moomintroll slowly. "You aren't a collector any longer, are you? Now you are just an owner. That's nowhere near as much fun."

"No," said the Hemulen, thoroughly dejected. "It is most decidedly nowhere near as much fun."

"SMALL Hemulens are very shy," Moomintroll explained with a whisper. "I think she is crocheting. It makes her feel safer."

MOOMINTROLL stared at the jagged black-and-yellow design of the Hemulen's coat. He wondered to himself why he didn't enjoy the Hemulen's company as he should.

After all the time he had spent wandering around on his own and longing for a companion that wasn't secretive and remote, but cheery and industrious – just like the Hemulen!

"MAMMA dear, we can't possibly take all of that with us. People will laugh!" said Moomintroll.

"It's cold in the Lonely Mountains," Moominmamma answered, slipping two more blankets, an umbrella and a frying pan into the bag. "Do you have a compass?"

"Yes," said Moomintroll. "But couldn't we at least leave out the plates? I thought we could eat off leaves."

Sweet, Sensitive Moomintroll

"My, my... he has got such a lot of feelings,
that Moomintroll!"

"You're angry, aren't you?" Moomintroll asked quietly. "I suppose you are terribly wild and cruel and ruthless, aren't you?... Well, there, there, there, you little rascal..."

"It is angry," thought Moomintroll. "So small and yet so angry. Now what should I do to get it to like me? What do you suppose it feeds on?"

MOOMINTROLL wrinkled his snout, but said nothing.

AFTER their conversation, Moomintroll was entirely too distraught to go directly home. Instead he strolled along the seashore, walking a long way out to circle the bathing-house and then back again.

"BY a cat's whisker, I'm sure no one could possibly be angry about something like that," assured Moomintroll.

"Go ahead and sing," muttered Moomintroll, cross and about to cry. "Sing about this horrible winter, with its black ice and its hostile snow-horses and other creatures that never appear, but hide away and are altogether strange."

Moomintroll trudged along up the slope, kicking snow as he went, the tears freezing on his snout. All of sudden, he began to sing a song of his own.

See here, you wretched cowards of this never-ending night,
You took away the sun and in its place brought freezing blight.
I stand alone, my feet are sore with cold and they do smart,
In vain I seek the green trees of the Valley in my heart.
For the seashore and the porch of blue I sorely reminisce,
Alas, for me, the misery of this snow is an abyss.

My wish would be to live within a sunflower big and sweet
And lie upon my belly in fine sand that gives off heat
And live each day contentedly with windows open wide
Towards the pretty garden and the buzzing bees outside.
I'd raise my eyes towards the clear blue sky that mustn't perish,
That keeper of the burning amber sun that I so cherish.

MOOMINTROLL sat staring down at the ice when suddenly he felt himself getting cross. It began in his stomach, like all strong emotions do. He felt as though he had been deceived.

"I won't promise anything," said Moomintroll in a grumpy manner and looked down at his soup-plate.

"Your mother was in a strange mood just now," said Sniff.

"Was she irritated or sad?" asked Moomintroll, astonished.

"I think she was more sad than angry," Sniff answered.

"In that case, I must go to her at once," said Moomintroll, and he stood up to leave. "Why, that is just awful."

"Aren't you all being unkind," said Moomintroll sadly.

JUST at that moment, the alarm clock began to ring. Moomintroll had set it to ring each night just as it was getting dark, because that was when he missed having company the most.

MOOMINTROLL sighed. He felt sad, even though he had no real reason to feel that way.

MOOMINTROLL
felt as if he were the
only creature in the
world. He had never
felt so alone. He ran
between the trees
and yelled her name,
listened, and then
ran again. At last he
stopped and looked at
the watch.

MOOMINTROLL kept waiting, but he was no longer so eager, just disappointed and tired.

Happiness and Dreams

At times he thought he could clearly see the trail that Snufkin had made on the sodden ground. The tracks skipped and danced here and there, and were difficult to follow. On occasion they took great leaps and even crossed paths. "He must have been feeling quite happy," thought Moomintroll. "I believe that right here he has even done a somersault."

"LITTLE MY!" cried Moomintroll, his mouth full of snow. He struggled to his feet, beside himself with delight and anticipation.

MOOMINTROLL curled up into a ball once again and put
his paws under his warm stomach. He let himself fall asleep.
His dreams were undulating and blue, like the nocturnal sea.

"MAMMA," he said, "there is so much I have to tell you..."

MOOMINTROLL found a large box in the attic. It was full of old paper cut-outs of flowers and decorations. He lapsed into longing admiration of their summer-like beauty… Then he thought to paste them on the walls. He did his pasting work slowly and carefully, so as to make his work last longer. He saved the prettiest pictures of all to paste on the wall above his sleeping mother.

" You are like Diana," Moomintroll said admiringly.

"Who is she?" asked the Snork Maiden, obviously flattered.

"She was the goddess of hunting," explained Moomintroll.

"As beautiful as the Wooden Queen and just as clever as you."

Communicating with Nature

MOOMINTROLL TRAVELLED EVERY CORNER OF
MOOMINVALLEY, WILD WITH PRIDE
AND EXPECTATION.

MOOMINTROLL said, "Did you know that if you fly hundreds and hundreds of miles up into the air that the sky is no longer blue? It is black as night way up there. Even during the day."

"I'VE had enough of your dark nights," yelled Moomintroll. "And no, I do not want to hear the chorus. I'm cold, I'm all alone, and I want the sun to come back!"

MOOMINTROLL watched the approach of the threatening weather, billowing in from afar. It felt as if a curtain had just fallen on a play, in preparation for the dramatic final scene to commence.

"THERE is water nearby," said Moomintroll, sniffing the air.
He took a step towards the wind that he smelled coming in
from the sea, and then he took another. Soon he began to run –
for there was nothing Moomintroll loved more than swimming.

"COME on, everyone! Get up! Let's go swimming!"
yelled Moomintroll.

Moomintroll had never experienced a blizzard before. He expected thunder and braced himself for the claps that he thought would sound.

But there came no crashing thunderbolts, nor even any lightning for that matter.

"I'm nothing but air and wind. I am a part of the storm itself," thought Moomintroll as he let himself go. "This is almost like in the summer, fighting against the waves of the sea. You bob along like a cork in the rainbow-coloured mist of the water, but the heavy surges keep pushing you back towards the shore. You end up being thrown back to the sandy beach, laughing and taken aback by it all."

THE falling snow was the only thing in sight. Moomintroll was overtaken by the same exhilaration that he felt each summer as he waded out for a swim in the sea.

"HOW horrid," said Moomintroll, picking his way gingerly through the melting snow.

"THE sun is coming back!" thought Moomintroll, excited. "No more darkness and solitude. Then I shall be able to sit on the veranda once again and warm my back in the sun…"

Suddenly the hairs on Moomintroll's back bristled. A thrill raced through his body as he watched a red glow gathering on the murky horizon. It condensed into a thin red streak, propelling its protracted rays out over the ice.

"There it is!" exclaimed Moomintroll.

He lifted Little My into the air and kissed her smack on the nose.

"Humph, don't be silly," said Little My. "There's nothing to make a fuss about."

"Oh yes there is!" yelled Moomin. "Spring is coming! It will be warm! Everyone will wake up!"

He picked up the fish from the ice and threw them high into the air. Then he did a headstand, right there on the ice. He had never felt so happy.

ONE by one, the snowflakes floated down on to his warm snout, and melted. He reached out to grab them so he could admire them for a fleeting moment. He looked towards the sky and watched them drift down towards him, more and more, as soft and light as a feather.

"So that's how it works," thought Moomintroll. "And I thought somehow that the snow grew from the ground up!"

MOOMINTROLL sat at the tip of the boat's prow and watched the ripples around him. It felt magnificent to look down into the deep green water, while *The Adventure* made white crests in her wake.

I believe that my son Moomintroll has inherited my weakness for the seashore. I am very proud when he dives for pearls, finds underwater caves, and discovers treasures that have washed up on shore after a storm.

"YIPPEE!" shouted Moomintroll. "We're going to an island!"

HOW wonderful to be a Moomin, to have just woken up, completely refreshed, and dance along on the bottle-green waves in the first light of morning!

MOOMINTROLL lay down and stretched himself out straight. He felt dizzy after staring for so long at the restless water swirling below.

MOOMINTROLL was convinced that winter had set out to crush him, to show him once and for all that he could not manage on his own. Earlier he had been magically draped in a shimmering cape of freshly falling snow. Just when he had started to like winter, it went and threw a raging blizzard right in his face.

THERE was a sense of expectation and melancholy in the air. The harvest moon shone enormous and odd in the sky. Moomintroll thought that the last weeks of the summer were the best, although he couldn't put his finger on just why.

A deep sadness welled up inside Moomintroll as he gazed about. He thought of how frightened everyone in the entire world must be right now to see the ball of fire approaching. He thought about the sea, the rain, the wind, the sunshine, the grass and the moss… and how it would be impossible to live without them.

Then he thought to himself, "But I am sure that Mamma will figure out a way to save us all."

"Now I've got everything," Moomintroll said to himself. "I've seen an entire year, winter too. I am the first Moomin to have experienced a full year in all its glory."

Small, Large and Important

"I'M THINKING ABOUT YOU AND ME GOING ON AN
EXPEDITION THAT WILL BE THE LONGEST WE'VE
EVER HAD."

"Now that I have some food in my stomach and have thought about it for a while, everything is a bit clearer."

"We are related. Mamma has always said that our forefathers lived behind the tiled stove."

"Mamma, wake up," Moomintroll cried. "Something altogether dreadful is happening. They call it Christmas."

"CHRISTMAS?"
repeated Moomintroll
in wonder. "Does he
eat?"

MOOMINTROLL was quiet for a moment. Then he told her, "Someone is carrying off things from our house."

"Well, that is probably a good thing," said Too-Ticky cheerfully. "You have too many things. And to think of all the other things that you remember, and the things you dream of!"

"I'M not sure that this went off as it was supposed to," said Moomintroll, with apprehension.

"WHAT is it?" said Moomintroll. Discoveries were his very favourite thing (after mysterious paths, swimming and secrets, that is).

"SOMETIMES people have to be alone," said Moomintroll. "You are still too small to understand."

"COULDN'T
you see that I was
feeling down?" asked
Moomintroll.

Too-Ticky shrugged
her shoulders. "Each
of us has to figure
things out for
ourselves," she replied,
"and overcome our
obstacles on our own."

"GIRLS are silly, and so are you," said Moomintroll. He burrowed down deep into his sleeping bag and turned towards the wall of the tent.

"WE'RE in luck," said Moomintroll. "The door is open. That goes to show that sometimes it's good to be careless!"

"SOME people sure do have troubles," thought Moomintroll. "The whole business about the jam isn't so awful, after all. The Sunday jars could still be hidden away – those with the strawberries from the garden. For the time being, anyway."

"WE have to bring provisions along," said Moomintroll.

Brave Moomintroll

MOOMINTROLL STOOD STILL FOR A MOMENT
AND BREATHED IN AND OUT AS PEACEFULLY
AS HE COULD.

"YOU mustn't lose your courage now," said Hemulen encouragingly. "Once more now!"

But the next time never came, because Moomintroll gave up. For a long time afterwards, Moomintroll imagined what it would have been like to jump a third, triumphant time. How he would have landed on the bridge after a beautiful sweeping curve, turned to the others and smiled. Everyone would have cheered with admiration. But it was not to be.

Instead Moomintroll said, "I'm going back home. You can continue as long as you want, but I'm going home."

"WHAT an exciting life we live," thought Moomintroll. "Everything could be turned upside down in a moment – for no reason whatsoever."

MOOMINTROLL wasn't frightened any longer, but he was so excited that he wasn't even able to drink his morning coffee.

"I think it's quite enough of an adventure to glide down a winding river," said Moomintroll. "You never know what's around the next bend."

MOOMINTROLL kept close behind Snufkin as they made their way through the forest. On both sides of the path, they could hear footsteps and shuffling. It was almost petrifying.

"What a lovely night," said a voice directly behind Moomintroll.

Moomintroll quickly summoned up all his courage and answered, "Yes, it is!" And just then he felt a little shadow move past him in the dark.

"DON'T you think this is just a little, just a teeny-bit dangerous?" whispered Moomintroll and put his paw in Pappa's.

MOOMINTROLL stared into the darkness. There was something out there. Little specks of light... palely lit creatures were moving back and forth between the sleepers. Moomintroll shook Snufkin awake.

"Look! Do you see?" he said in terror. "Ghosts!"

"LOOK at that!" whispered Moomintroll. "There are secret marks everywhere! Some of them are almost one hundred metres in the air! Do you know what I think? You have stumbled upon a haunted path, Sniff, and the spooks are now trying to lead us astray. What do you think of that?"

MOOMINTROLL warmed his back, but then his stomach was cold. The whole world seemed to be dancing a waltz around him, teasing him.

"ISN'T it strange," said Moomintroll, "that we who are going directly towards the most dangerous place are less frightened than those who are leaving it?"

THE Snork Maiden stood with her ears drooping.
Moomintroll pressed his snout against hers and said,
"There's no need to pretend that you are radiantly beautiful,
because you are. Don't worry, we can play 'damsel in
distress' tomorrow instead."

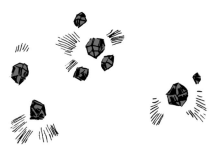

"WE are sure to find some new treasures tomorrow," said
Moomintroll consolingly. "No sense being sad about it any
longer. Let's get a move on now, Sniff, it's getting cold."

Praise, Encouragement and Happy Times

MOOMINTROLL WOULD SAY AT ONCE THAT IT WAS A
GOOD SONG. A REALLY, REALLY GOOD ONE.

FOR the first time in a long while, Moomintroll went in and took a long look at his sleeping Mamma and Pappa. Then he held the lamp up high over the Snork Maiden and gazed at her thoughtfully. Her fringe gleamed in the lamplight; he saw that she was unbearably sweet.

"A toast to Mamma and Pappa!" said Moomintroll, and drained his glass. (At that very same moment, Moominpappa was aboard the floating theatre, raising his glass to drink a toast to his son: "To the safe return of Moomintroll!" he said solemnly.)

"DEAREST Mamma, I am so terribly fond of you,"
said Moomintroll.

They strolled down to the bridge, but no mail had
arrived. The evening sun threw long shadows across the
valley and a sense of peace and serenity prevailed.

"HOW nice it feels to be good," the small Hemulen
thought docilely. Moominmamma squeezed Moomintroll's
paw in hers.

MOOMINTROLL took a step forward in amazement. Yes, there was no doubt about it. The Groke was happy to see him. She didn't mind about the hurricane lamp at all. She was simply glad that Moomintroll had come to greet her.

"GOOD gracious!" said an astonished Moomintroll. "It was only a game! I really am very happy that you think so much of me, though."

MOOMINTROLL turned to Hemulen. His bad conscience made him say something friendly:

"It must be nice to enjoy the cold water."

"Why, it is the best thing I know," answered the Hemulen, beaming. "It fends off all sorts of useless thoughts and imaginings. Believe you me: nothing is as dangerous as staying cooped up inside."

"Is that so?" said Moomin.

"That's right. Staying inside gives rise to all sorts of senseless ideals," Hemulen explained.

MAMMA sat on the veranda steps waiting. She was holding something in her paw and she looked very pleased and expectant.

"Can you guess what this is?" she asked.

"Is it a dinghy?" said Moomintroll. He laughed out loud – not because anything was funny, mind you, but because he was so incredibly happy.

"IT'S for me," thought Moomintroll. "It must be for me. Mamma always makes the first tree-bark dinghy of the season for the one she holds most dear. Then she covers the whole thing up a bit when she gives it, so the others won't feel bad."

PERHAPS the happiest one of all was Moomintroll, who walked home with his mother through the garden, just as the moon was fading into dawn. The trees were swaying slowly in the morning breeze rising up from the sea.

TONIGHT we are all going to climb into bed and begin our winter hibernation. (All Moomins are known to do this sometime in November, and in this respect they act most wisely, for they do not enjoy the cold or the dark.)

The End